50 UNIQUE PHYSICS PROBLEMS

S.Nishanth Vikraman

Cover design by: Manasa, Rithika
Illustrations by: Manasa, Rohit Chari, Rithika, Yuvaraja

To Mom, Dad and Reethika

CONTENTS

PREFACE

This book of physics problems is specifically curated such that it would, I hope, be capable of testing the student's understanding of various physical phenomena, especially when multiple topics are involved simultaneously. There are some problems based on everyday practical observations, and also some on interesting hypothetical scenarios. Whilst some problems end with simple intuition, some are solved with clever calculus and some others I couldn't solve beyond the differential equation! It is suited for the aspiring high school physics student and perhaps even the undergraduate fresher, albeit it not being intended for any academic preparatory purposes. A thorough understanding of high school physics and multivariate calculus is recommended. The 50 problems are arranged in an increasing order of difficulty, and the problems are thematically grouped in the next section for your reference. Elements of some of the problems may have been derived from various sources, particularly from those pertaining to the IITJEE examinations, all of which might be near impossible to attribute.

THEMATIC PROBLEM ORDER

The problems have all been grouped by the major concept(s) involved and are listed below:

Kinematics: 33, 34, 35, 40, 47, 48
Dynamics: 1, 3, 5, 6, 8, 11, 12, 13, 15, 16, 20, 22, 23, 24, 25, 26, 27, 28, 29, 38, 39, 43, 44, 49, 50
Rotational Mechanics: 2, 3, 6, 13, 14, 18, 23, 29, 43, 44, 50
Fluid Mechanics: 4, 5, 7, 9, 11, 12, 13, 14, 15, 16, 19, 22, 29, 30, 32, 34, 35, 38, 42
Thermodynamics: 10, 17, 24, 39
Ray Optics: 33, 36, 37, 41, 47, 48, 49
Wave Optics: 21
Gravitation: 1, 4, 9, 11, 12, 22, 31, 50
Wave Mechanics: 45
Elasticity: 30, 45
Simple Harmonic Motion: 5, 7
Elecronics: 6, 10, 25, 26, 27, 28
Electromagnetism: 6, 18, 20, 25, 26, 27, 44, 50
Electrostatics: 2, 19
Ideal Gas: 1, 11, 12, 22, 32, 38, 43

PROBLEMS

◆ ◆ ◆

P1 Consider a planet of mass M_p and radius R_p with an ideal gaseous atmosphere, with the average molar mass of the air being M and ambient temperature being T. Find the orbit radius for a cubical satellite of face area A so that it does the least work during orbit.

P2 A dielectric with a dielectric constant dependant on x and y as $K(x,y)$ is fixed between a square parallel plate capacitor, as shown below. Find the capacitance of this arrangement.

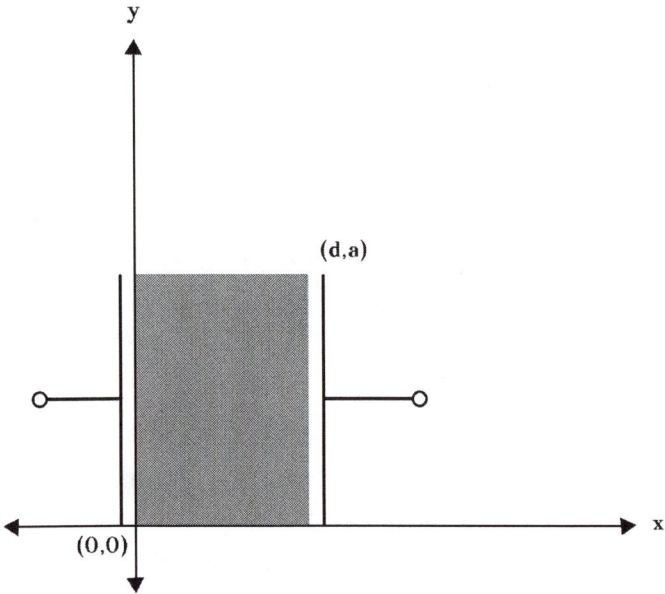

P3 A small sphere of radius r is placed inside a sufficiently rough spherical track of radius R. Find the minimum velocity that must be imparted to the small sphere to make it complete one full revolution around the track.

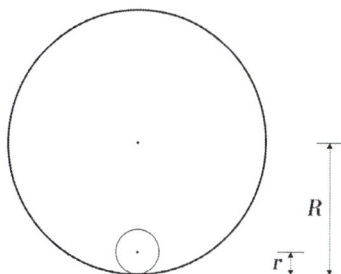

P4 Find the height risen by a liquid column (specific density ρ) in a massive barometer kept at the surface of a planet of mass M, radius R and ground level pressure P_0.

P5 A horizontal water (of density ρ) jet of volume flow rate λ and outlet cross-sectional area A is directed onto a vertical plate (of mass m) which is connected to an ideal spring of spring constant k attached to a wall. Assuming that the vertical motion of the plate is restricted and that the plate is large enough that the jet always hits it throughout its motion, find out the time period of the resulting horizontal SHM. Does this depend on the distance of the jet's outlet from the plate?

P6 A rod of mass m and length r is hinged onto the centre of a circular conducting track of same radius. This track arrangement is then kept inside an inductive coil of inductance L. The hinged point of the rod and the circular track are then connected in series with an ideal DC power supply of voltage V and to the coil. If the circuit is closed at time $t = 0$, find the differential equation(s) governing the motion of the rod.

P7 A sufficiently large rod is placed on triangular rails and it is then dipped in a soap solution and the other end is fitted to a spring of spring constant k as shown below. Find the time period of SHM of the system.

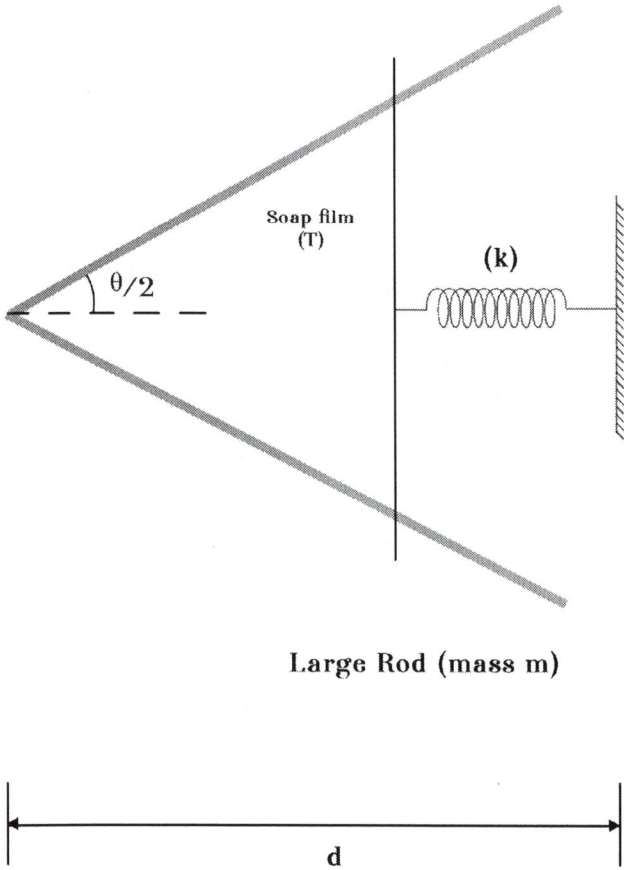

Soap film
(T)

(k)

$\theta/2$

Large Rod (mass m)

d

P8 A constant force **F** acts on the point X in the door (mass m) as shown (top view). Find the direction of this force so that it rotates the door by an angle of 90° :

i.   *in the quickest time.*

ii.   *by doing least amount of work.*

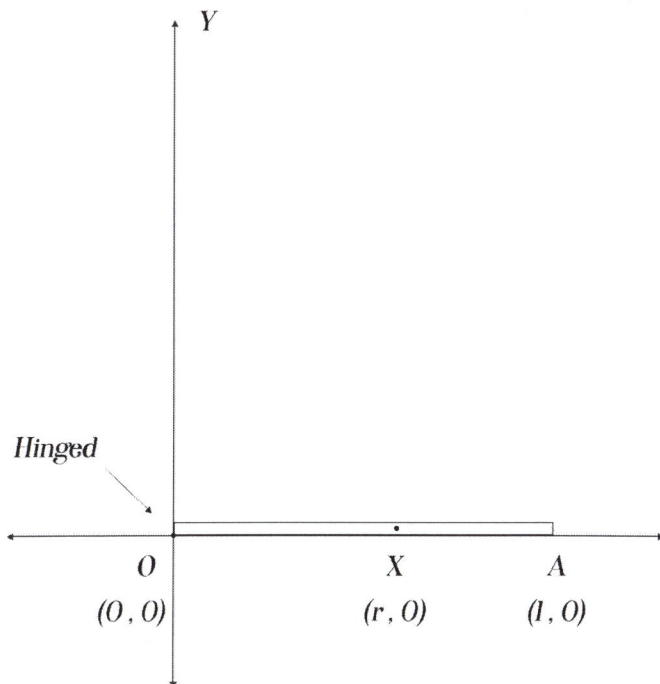

P9 A downward facing tap with a circular outlet (radius r) is opened to let water (density ρ) flow out continuously with a flow rate Q. Neglecting the ground, find the 3-dimensional shape of the water column.

P10 A resistor of mass m, initial resistance R_0, specific heat capacity s and coefficient of thermal resistance y is connected to an ideal voltage supply of rating V. Find the functional dependence of the resistance versus time.

P11 Consider the planet described in **P1**. A soap bubble of surface tension S and initial radius R_0 is imparted with a velocity u radially outwards at time $t=0$. Find the differential equation which models its distance from the centre with respect to time.

P12 Consider the planet described in **P1**. Find the governing differential equations of the motion of a spherical body of drag coefficient C, mass m and radius r_s; if it is thrown with speed u radially outwards.

P13 A cylindrical container of mass M_C, radius R and height H is filled with an ideal fluid of density ρ and kept on a rough surface of coefficient of friction μ. Identify the range of positions wherein making an orifice of area a ($a \ll \pi r^2$) would result in the container toppling instead of translatory motion.

P14 A cylindrical container of height H, radius r and areal density σ is filled up to height L ($L<H$) with an ideal fluid of density ρ and rotated about an axis passing through the centres of the circular faces of the container with an angular speed ω. Find the moment of inertia of the system about the rotational axis.

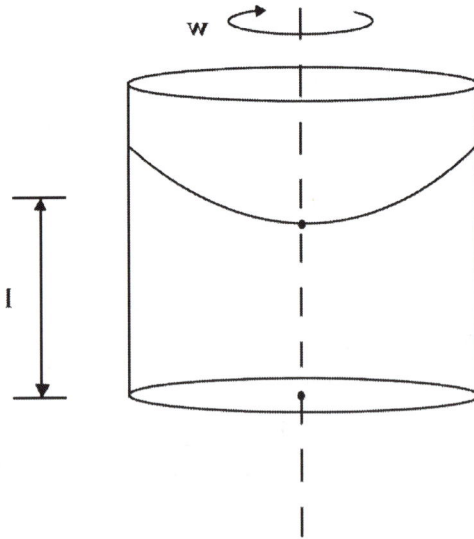

P15 A cylindrical container of height H and radius R is filled fully with an ideal fluid of specific density ρ and an external force accelerates it at a constant value of a. Now a spherical ball of radius r and specific density σ is just dropped at the surface of the fluid at the centre of the container. Find the values of the container's acceleration a so that the ball has its first collision with the bottom face of the container.

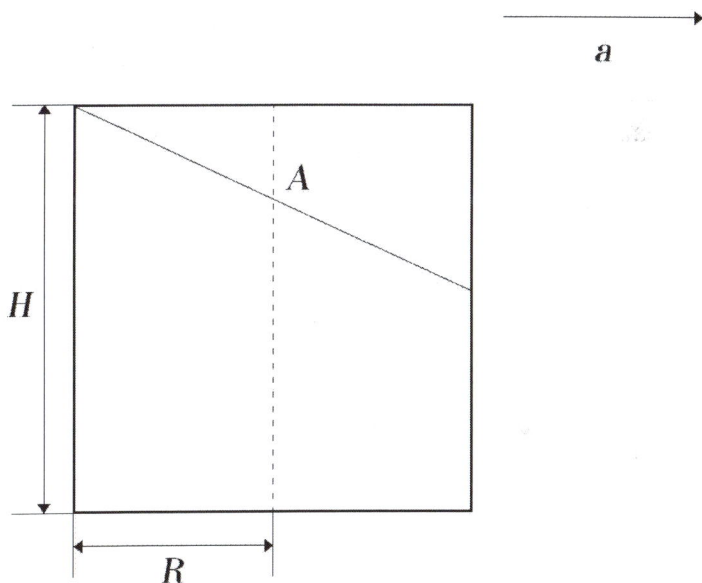

P16 The vacuum in a barometer's measuring tube is just set up on an ideal fluid of specific density ρ. Considering this as time $t = 0$, find the time taken by the fluid to reach its equilibrium height h inside the barometer. The surrounding atmospheric pressure is P_0.

P17 A cubical container of length a is filled with n_0 moles of an ideal gas and the temperature inside the container is maintained as a spatial function $T(x, y, z)$ using external means (cube is placed fully in the first octant with one of its corners as the origin). Find the pressure of the gas inside.

P18 A spherical ball of mass m is charged to $+q$ and is attached to a string of length l. This is now fixed to a rigid support and a conical pendulum is set up, making an angle θ_0 with the vertical and the bob is rotating with a tangential velocity of v_0. Now a magnetic field of magnitude B is applied vertically upwards. Find the final tangential speed of the bob.

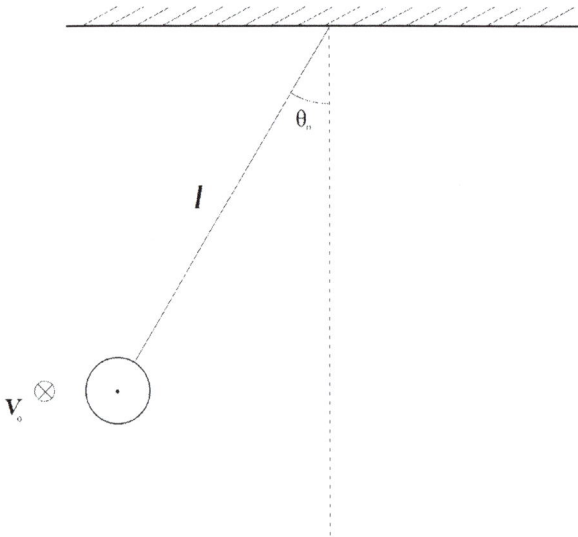

P19 A cylindrical capacitor of inner cylinder radius a, outer cylinder radius b, and length l is closed on one end and the open end is just placed on the surface of a liquid of density ρ kept in a large container. If the capacitor is charged to Q and the volume inside the capacitor is vacuumed out, find the height of the liquid column risen inside the capacitor. Take atmospheric pressure to be P_0.

P20 Consider an infinitely long solid conducting cylinder of radius R carrying a constant current i. A point charge $+Q$ which is initially at h distance away from the axis of the cylinder is now given a velocity v directed towards the axis. Considering the axis of the cylinder as the y-axis and the perpendicular from the cylinder's axis to the initial position of the charge as the x-axis, find the trajectory of the point charge.

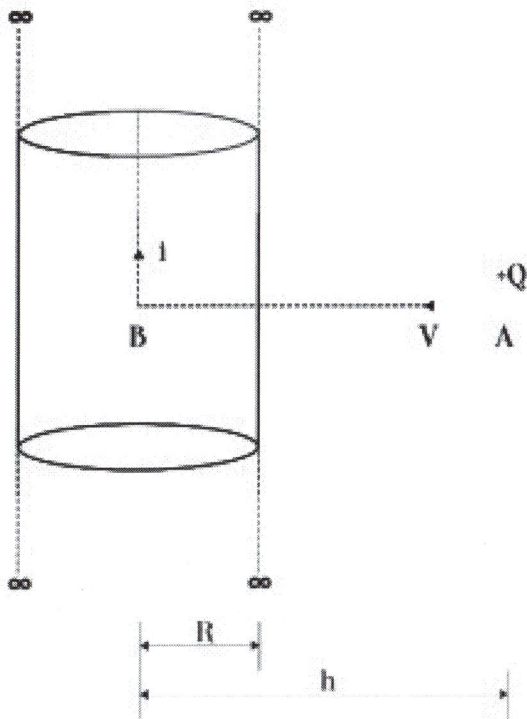

P21 The screen in the conventional Double Slit Experiment is now replaced with a mirror and the screen is now placed behind the monochromatic light source of wavelength λ and intensity I_0 (the light source is directed only to the two slits). Examine the nature of interference produced and deduce the value of light intensity as a function of position in the new screen.

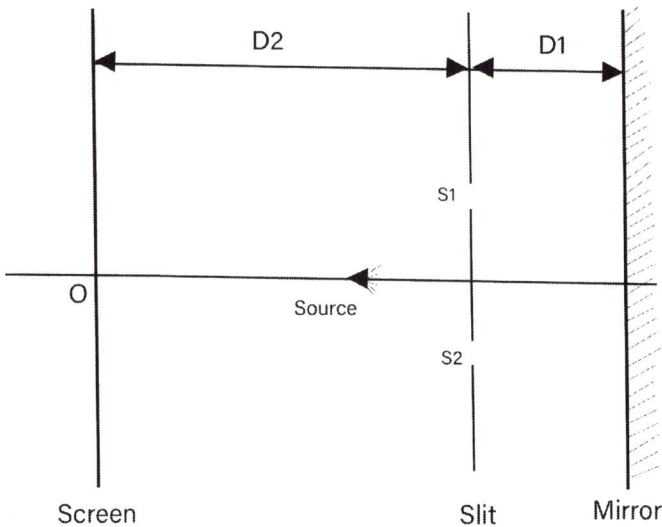

P22 Consider a planet described in **P1**. A spherical drop of water of specific density ρ, radius r and Henry's constant for dissolution of gases K_H starts to fall from a distance h away from the centre of the planet. Assuming that the shape doesn't alter and the dissolution of atmospheric gases doesn't cause any volumetric changes, find the drop's speed as a function of distance from the planet's centre.

P23 An elliptical track of semi-major and semi-minor axis lengths being a and b respectively is oriented such that the minor axis is along the vertical direction. Find the time taken by a spherical ball which is given a tangential speed u as shown below to complete a full revolution around the track. Assume u is sufficiently big enough and the track is sufficiently rough to maintain pure rolling always.

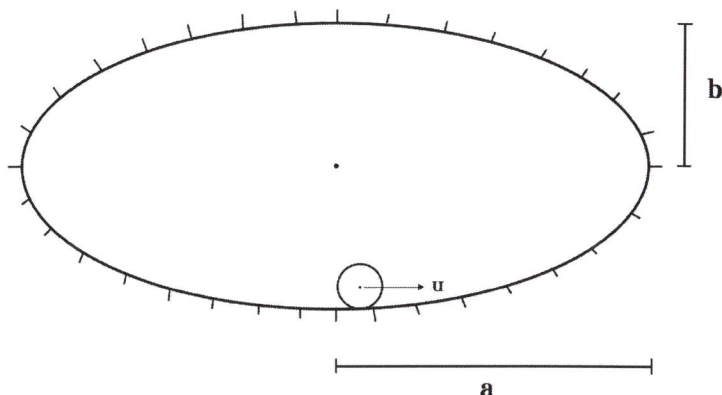

P24 A cubical ice block at of length a, density ρ and latent heat of fusion L_f is imparted with a horizontal speed of u on a flat plane with a coefficient of friction μ at $t = 0$. Assuming the atmospheric temperature to be 273 K and all frictional heat produced is directly used to melt the ice, find the differential equation governing the motion of the ice cube.

P25 An ideal DC voltage source of potential difference V is connected in series with a resistance R and a moving rod on rail arrangement as shown in the diagram. Find the differential equation that governs the motion of the rod. (Include the magnetic field induced by the wires)

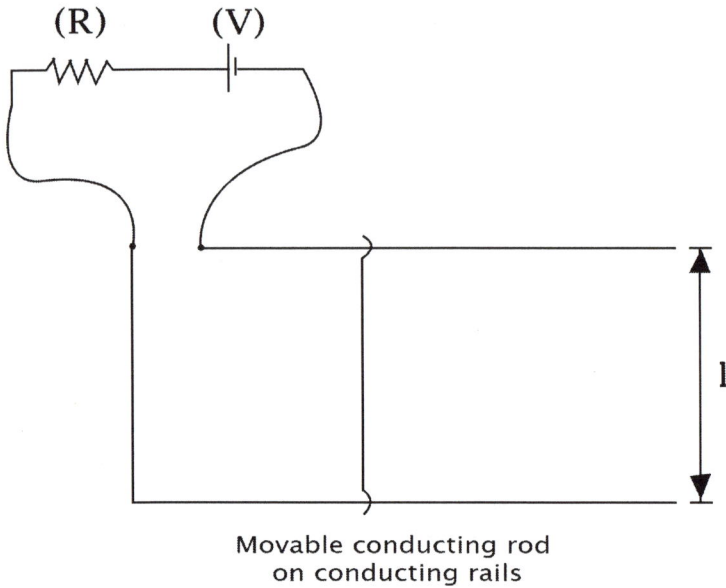

(R)   (V)

l

Movable conducting rod
on conducting rails

P26 One of the plates of a parallel plate capacitor is fixed to a moving rod kept on conducting rails and the capacitor (capacitance C) is connected in series to a resistor of resistance R. If the capacitor is charged to Q and a magnetic field of constant intensity B into the plane of the paper is switched on at time $t = 0$ and the system is released, find the differential equation governing the motion of the rod as a function of time.

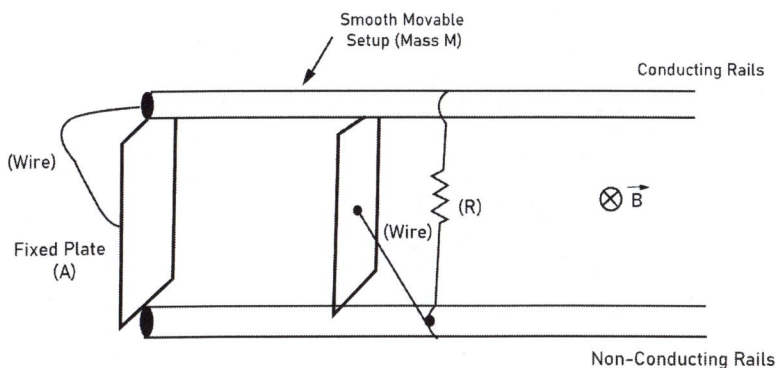

Smooth Movable Setup (Mass M)

Conducting Rails

(Wire)

Fixed Plate (A)

(R)

(Wire)

$\otimes \vec{B}$

Non-Conducting Rails

P27 An ideal DC voltage source of potential difference V is connected in series with an inductor of initial inductance L_0 and spring constant k (such an element to be referred as an inducto-spring henceforth) and a moving rod (mass m) on rails arrangement as shown. Find the differential equation governing the motion of the rod if a magnetic field of constant intensity B into the plane of the paper is switched on and the circuit closed at time $t = 0$.

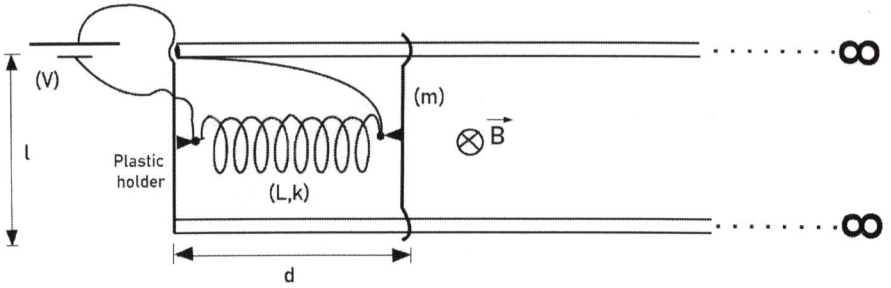

P28 An inductospring of initial inductance L_0 and spring constant k is connected in series to a parallel plate capacitor through a moving rod (mass m) on rails arrangement as shown. Find the differential equation governing the motion of the rod, if the capacitor is charged to Q at the beginning and the system is released.

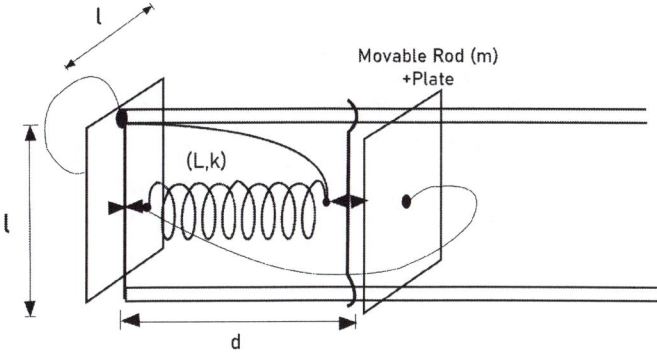

P29 A rod of cross sectional area A, length l and density λ is held such that one of its ends is just touching the surface of a reservoir of a liquid of density ρ and the rod makes an angle α with the horizontal. Assuming that the depth of the reservoir is sufficient and that the rod is denser than the liquid, find the differential equation(s) that govern the motion of the rod till it is submerged completely, if it is released from this state at time $t = 0$.

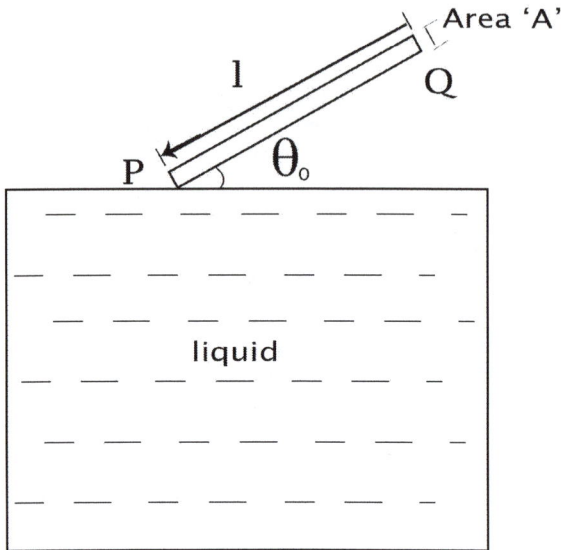

P30 A cuboidal container of base length l and breadth b is filled up to height H with a fluid of specific density ρ and bulk modulus B. If the container is given a constant acceleration of a, find the shape of the fluid's surface; provided that the container is large enough to prevent spillage and a is such that the surface doesn't reach the base of the container.

P31 Consider an atmosphere-less planet of mass M_p and radius R_p. A large piece of wire of mass M, cross-sectional area A, unstretched length l_0 and Young's modulus Y is kept vertically on the surface of the planet. Find the required escape velocity for the wire from this orientation.

P32 A cylindrical container of radius R and length L is filled with an ideal liquid of specific density ρ and the rest of the container is filled with n moles of ideal gas maintained in polytropic conditions $PV^a = K$, where K is a real constant. If a hole of area A $(A<<\pi R^2)$ is made at the bottom of the container, find the time taken to empty the liquid from the container; provided atmospheric pressure is P_0.

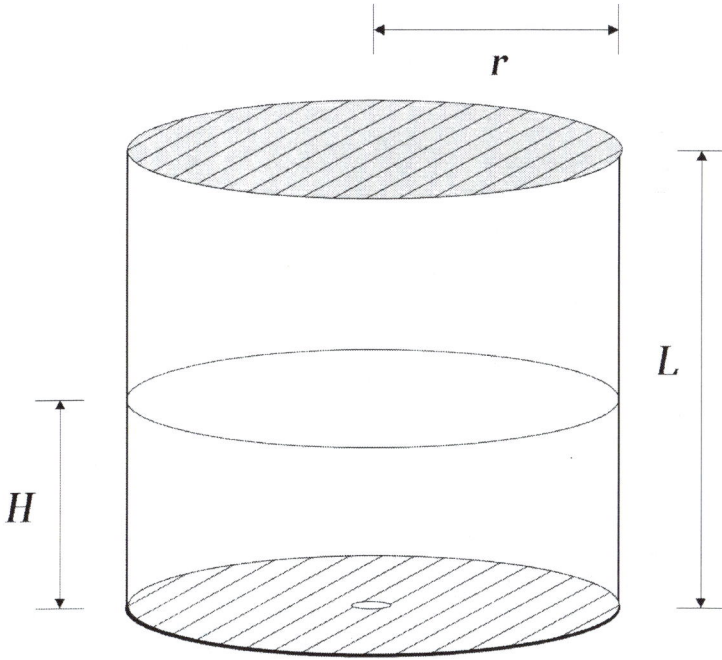

P33 A particle is moving towards a concave mirror of focal length f along its axis with a speed v_0 at time $t = 0$. If its deceleration described by $a = -v$, where v denotes the distance of the image of the particle formed by the mirror, from the mirror, at that instant, find the minimum initial distance of separation between the particle and the concave mirror so that the particle comes to rest before collision with the mirror.

P34 A stationary cylindrical container of radius R and height H is filled with an ideal fluid of density ρ. A slit is now made on the circumference of the container, along an arc of angle θ and through the entire length of the container. If this system is released at time $t = 0$, find the time taken by the fluid to empty the container.

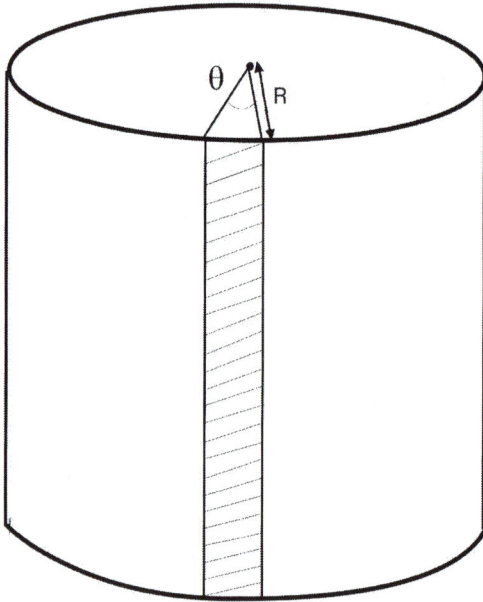

P35 A cuboidal container of length l is filled up to H height with a liquid of density ρ and is now given a constant acceleration of a in one direction. If a hole of area S is made at the bottom left point in this state, find the time taken to empty the container.

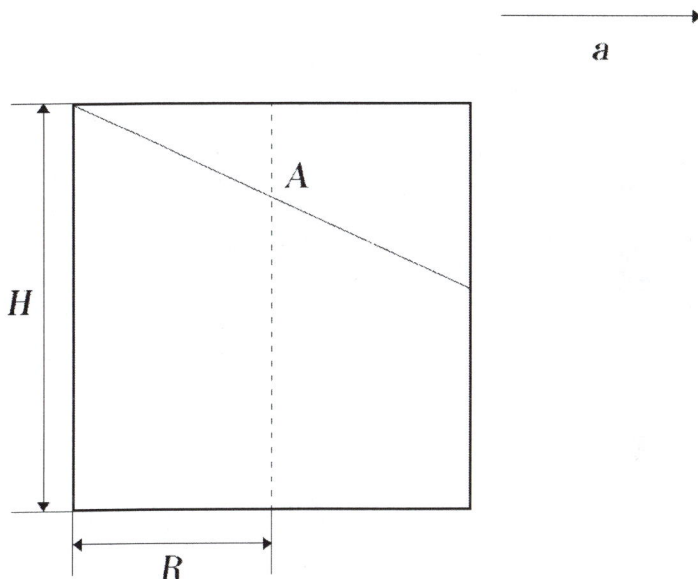

P36 A planet of radius R_p and mass M_p is at a distance d from a point source of light. The planet has an atmosphere whose refractive index varies with the distance from the centre of the planet R as:

$$\mu(R) = \mu_0 + \frac{Rd}{R^2 + d^2}$$

If the planet undergoes uniform rotation such that its time period is T, find the total daytime for any point on the planet.

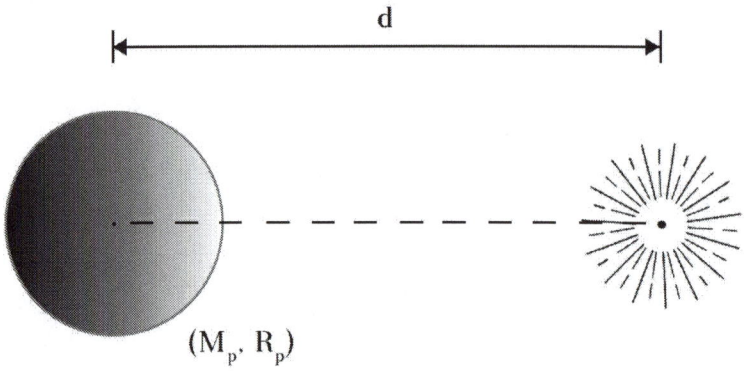

(M_p, R_p)

P37

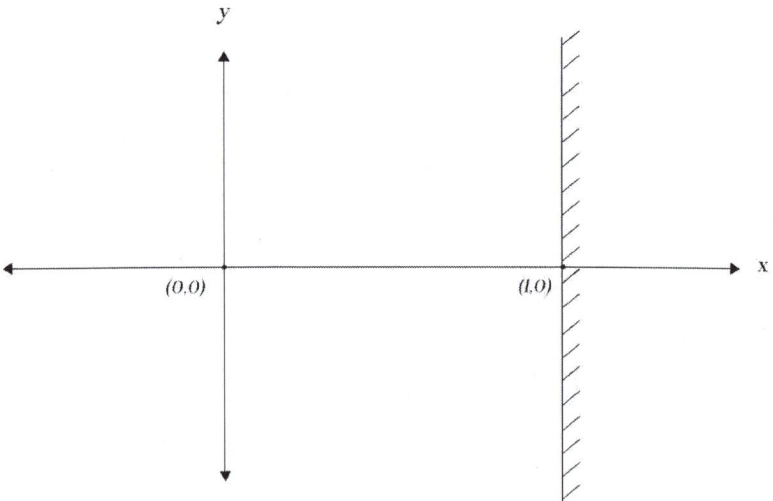

1) Consider a xy plane and let a plane mirror be kept at $(l, 0)$

perpendicular to the x axis.

a) A point particle is kept at the origin. Find the nearest point of the corresponding image to the origin for the corresponding variable refractive indices:

i. $\mu(x) = \sqrt{1 + x}$

ii. $\mu(y) = \sqrt{1 + |y|}$

b) A rod is kept from $(-h, 0)$ to $(0, 0)$. Find the nearest point of the corresponding image to the origin if the refractive index varies as

$$\mu(x) = \sqrt{1 + x}$$

2) Now a concave mirror of diameter d is kept at $(l, 0)$ with its axis oriented along x axis and a point particle is kept at origin. Find the nearest point of the corresponding image to the origin if the refractive index varies as

$$\mu(x) = \sqrt{1 + x}$$

P38 A cylinder of radius r is filled with n_1 moles of a fluid of specific density ρ and Henry's constant for dissolution of gases K_H up to a height L. A movable piston head of mass M is fixed at a height H from the base ($H > L$) and now apart from the fluid, the container houses n_2 moles of an ideal gas at constant temperature T_0. If the piston head is released, find:

a) The speed of the piston head as a function of time.

b) After reaching equilibrium, if the piston head is displaced by a small distance, find the time period of the resulting oscillations.

c) The value of Enthalpy for the gas dissolution process for one mole of gas.

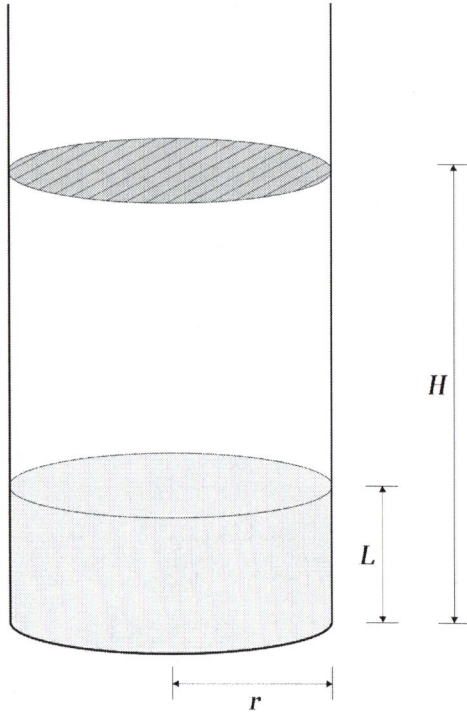

P39 A cubical block of side length a, density ρ, specific heat capacity s and latent heat of sublimation L_s is kept on the top of a rough inclined plane of incline angle θ, incline length l and coefficient of friction μ. If the initial temperature of the block is T and the sublimation temperature of the block is T_s, answer the following questions, assuming that all of the heat energy released due to the friction in the block sliding down the incline is used to heat the block up:

a) The incline angle θ after which the block doesn't sublime before reaching the bottom of the incline.

b) The incline angle θ (which is lower than the one calculated in part (a)) at which the block reaches the bottom in the quickest time.

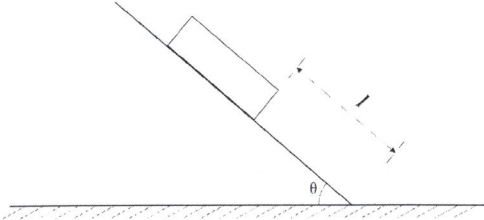

P40 A circular shaped pool of radius r filled with water is rotating at a constant angular speed ω about its centre. A swimmer can swim at constant speed v_s. In order to reach the diametrically opposite end of the pool, calculate the angle with the radial line to the start point with which the swimmer has to set off, and find the time taken for this process as well.

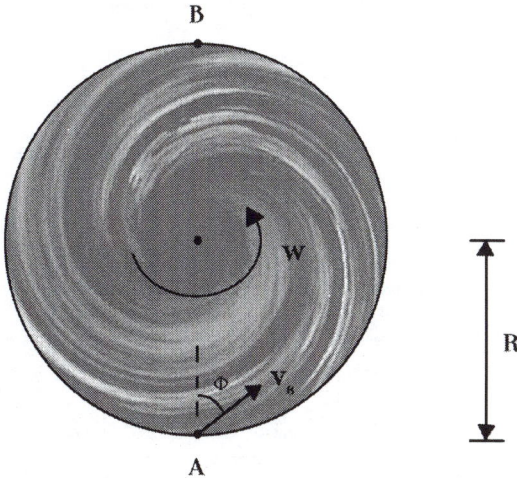

P41 A spherical blob of material of refractive index n_o and radius r_o is centred at the origin, while the refractive index of all of the remaining regions is μ_o

a) Find the locus of points outside the sphere from where the origin can be seen.

b) The initial spherical blob is removed and a new spherical blob of radius equal to the radius of the locus found in part (a) and of refractive index equal to the product of n_o and the ratio of the radii of the new and initial blobs is constructed at the origin.

$$R_1 = (R_0)_{locus}$$

$$n_1 = n_0\left(\frac{R_1}{R_0}\right)$$

This procedure is repeated m times so that:

$$R_{j+1} = (R_j)_{locus}$$

$$n_{j+1} = n_0\left(\frac{R_{j+1}}{R_j}\right)$$

Find the value of $\sum_0^m R_i$

P42 A liquid drop (density ρ, surface tension T) is resting on a surface with contact angle θ. Assuming that it is radially symmetric, find the differential equation governing the shape of the drop.

P43 A hollow cylinder of radius R and length L has a tangentially directed square hole of area a near its periphery at the centre of its length, as shown below. This hole is covered, and the cylinder is filled with an ideal gas of initial pressure P_i and initial density ρ_i, and kept on a sufficiently rough surface, such that the hole is at the topmost position. If the hole is opened at $t=0$, find the linear distance traversed as a function of time.

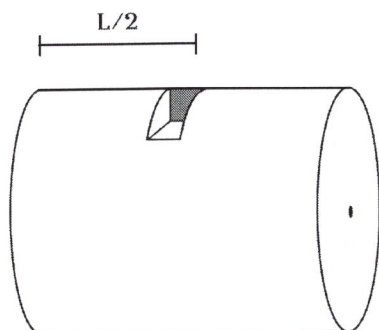

(Square with length a)

P44 A cylindrical capacitor of inner cylinder radius a, outer cylinder radius b, and length l (assume length is considerably greater than the radii) is charged to Q Coulombs. A magnetic field B is applied along the axis of the capacitor. If a point mass m possessing a charge $+q$ is brought to the surface of the inner capacitor at the centre of its length at $t=0$, find:

a) The time taken for it to reach the outer cylinder.

b) Angular distance covered due to the above process.

c) Launch speed and angle so that it starts orbiting about the centre of the cylindrical plates.

P45 A cylindrical capacitor of inner and outer cylinder radius as a and b respectively and length l is charged to Q, kept in vertical orientation, and then filled fully with a fluid of dielectric constant K and specific density ρ. At time $t=0$, a hole of area a is made at the bottom. Find the time taken to empty the cylindrical capacitor.

P46 A rope of initial mass per unit length α, initial unstretched length l, cross-sectional area A and Young's modulus of elasticity Y is held taut vertically by two supports such that the supports exert a tension T_e (note that this is apart from the tension due to the self-weight of the rope). If oscillations of frequency f and total energy E_0 are introduced into the rope such that standing waves are set up, Find:

a) The relation between the given parameters for standing waves to be possible.

b) The resulting standing wave equation.

P47 A line source of sound of frequency f_0 and length l is half submerged in water (refractive index μ). An observer is at d_0 distance away from the source and at the interface between air and water. If the source starts moving along the water with a speed v_s away from the observer, find the sound frequencies heard by the observer as a function of time.

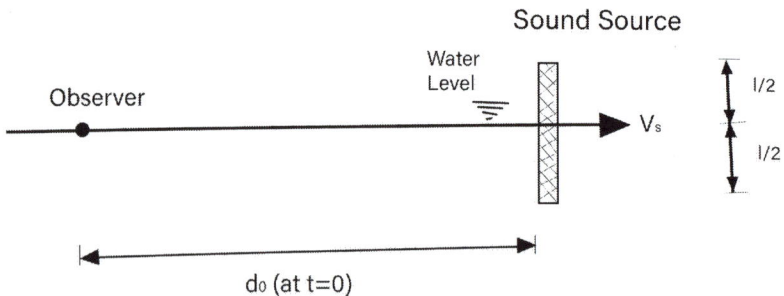

P48 A car is heading to a large obstacle with initial speed u. When the car is at distance l from the obstacle, the driver decides to stop the car according to the frequency of the sound reflected from the obstacle that he/she receives after sounding his/her horn with the retardation being:

$$a = -Kf_r$$

where f_r stands for reflected sound frequency and K is an appropriately dimensioned positive real number. Assuming l to be sufficiently large to avoid collisions, find the speed of the car a function of time.

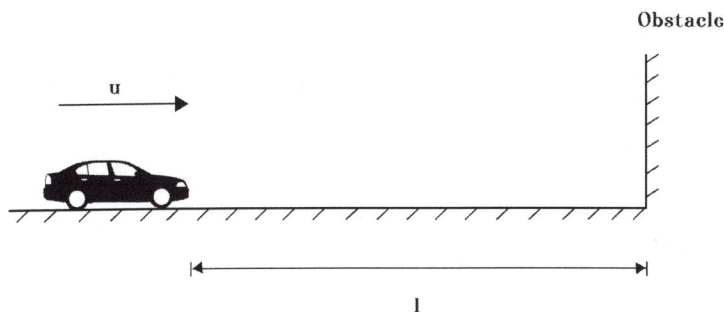

P49 An adiabatic piston-cylinder arrangement is filled with n moles of an ideal gas at initial temperature T_0 and pressure P_0 and held such that the weight of the piston (W) is of higher magnitude than the force acting on the piston due to the pressure of the gas. If a sound source of frequency f and a detector is placed on the interior surface of the piston and the piston is released from this state at time $t = 0$, find the equations governing the sound frequencies received by the detector as a function of time.

P50 Consider a planet of mass M and radius R. Assume it possesses an inherent magnetic field akin to a huge bar magnet of magnetic moment λ kept along the rotational axis of the planet. Now consider a charged particle of charge $+q$ and mass m and answer the following questions:

a) The escape velocity for the particle from the planet's surface.

b) The orbital speed required for an orbit of radius R_o about the equator of the planet.

c) Suppose the particle is thrown vertically from the equator with speed u (which is lower than the escape velocity.

    a. Find its speed as a function of radial distance from the planet.

    b. Find the maximum radial distance it reaches from the planet.

    c. Find the time taken before it lands for the first time.

    d. Find the angular displacement of the particle after landing from its initial position from which it was thrown.

d) Find the speed and the angle with the horizontal with which the particle must be launched so that it starts orbiting the planet (part b) at steady state.

AFTERWORD

I hope you were satisfied with this book's content. I have tried my best to make it as error free as possible, but if there be any errors, doubts or queries, feel free to contact me through email (nishanth.vik@gmail.com). I have also included **solutions** to some of the problems in the QR code below and I am also in the process of expanding it:

ACKNOWLEDGEMENTS

I am grateful to God for making this book come to fruition, from compiling problems as a hobby till publishing it.

Thanks to mom, dad and Reethika for their constant suppport and encouragement.

I am grateful to Manasa for her help in the publishing process, illustrations and cover design; Rithika for the cover design and illustrations; and Rohit and Yuvaraja for the illustrations.

Big Thanks to all my teachers and professors who have and are expanding the boundaries of my knowledge.

Thanks also to all my friends who have been supportive throughout.

Made in the USA
Monee, IL
08 January 2025

76388568R00024